ISN'T PROGRESS WONDERFUL?

STAN EALES

GRUB STREET • LONDON

Published by Grub Street
The Basement, 10 Chivalry Road
London SW11 1HT

British Library Cataloguing in Publication Data
Eales, Stan
Isn't Progress Wonderful? : the first book of eco-humour

I. Title
828.91409

ISBN 0-948817-48-8

Printed and bound in Italy by New Interlitho

DEDICATED TO MOTHER EARTH

AAYYAAYYAAARGH!!

'Come on in....the water's horrible'

'I wish Charlie wasn't so conscientious
about being a lumberjack'

'I don't care what the doctor said,
refined men do not eat unrefined food'

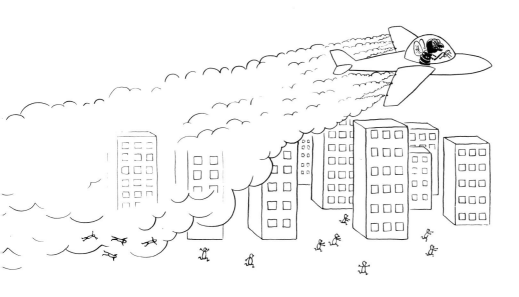

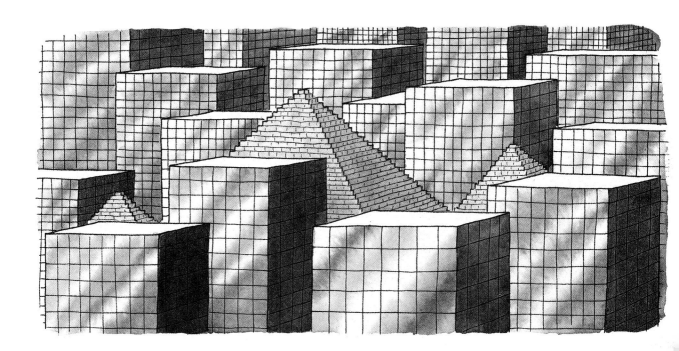

AFTER
TENNIEL

'Yeah, I would pay more tax
to have cleaner air'

'But hunting never hurt anyone'

'I'm going to put you on a course of antibiotics
— I recommend eating beef three times a day'

'I can hear the roar of traffic'

'Hey you bastard — this false beard is made from real fur'

'Hey hang on — we've already done this one'

'I hereby declare open this nuclear fuels processing plant'

'I am the ghost of environment future'

'Look – designer pollution'

'They reckon I've got heavy metal poisoning'

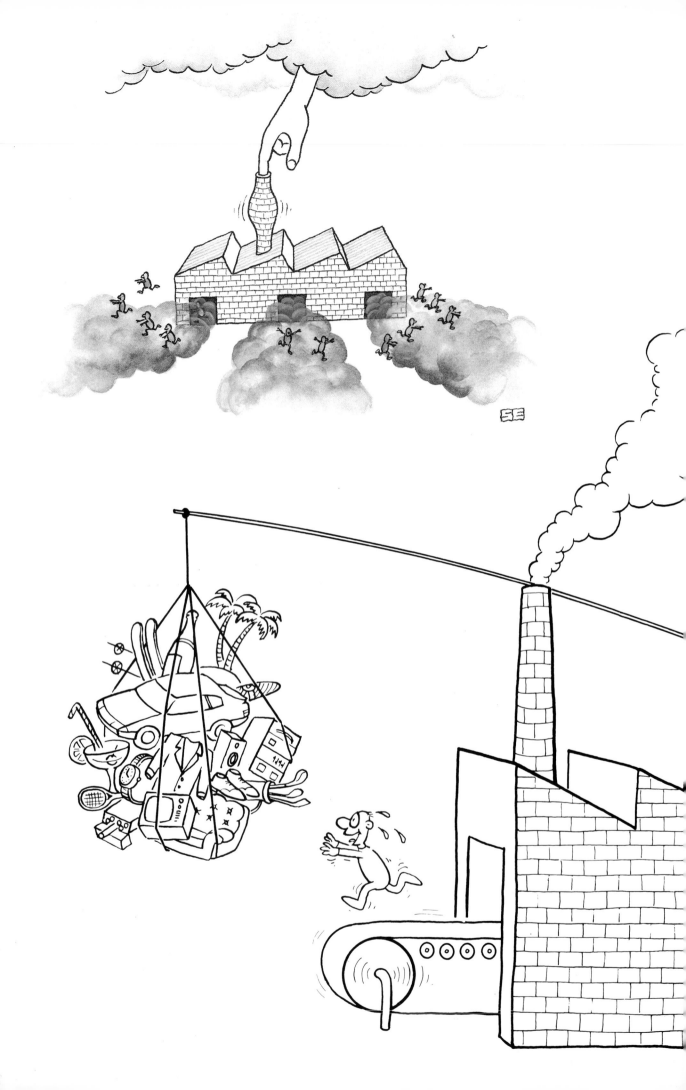

Haaoooooooooooooolll...... Haaooooooooooooooolll...... Haaoo

'We volunteered to test
the world's first
biodegradable condom'

I SIMPLY ADORE
YOUR RAINFOREST
COFFEE TABLE BOOK
AND MATCHING
RAINFOREST
COFFEE TABLE

'I just think that its been badly art directed'

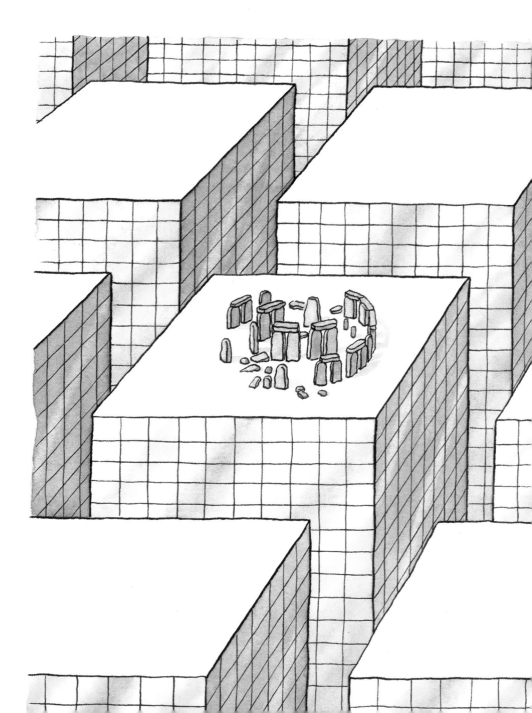

'What's worse than realizing that we will die someday,
is realizing that we're not terribly alive as it is'

'I used to be a Rodin
but I got left out
in the acid rain'

'It says here that he was the inventor
of the internal combustion engine'

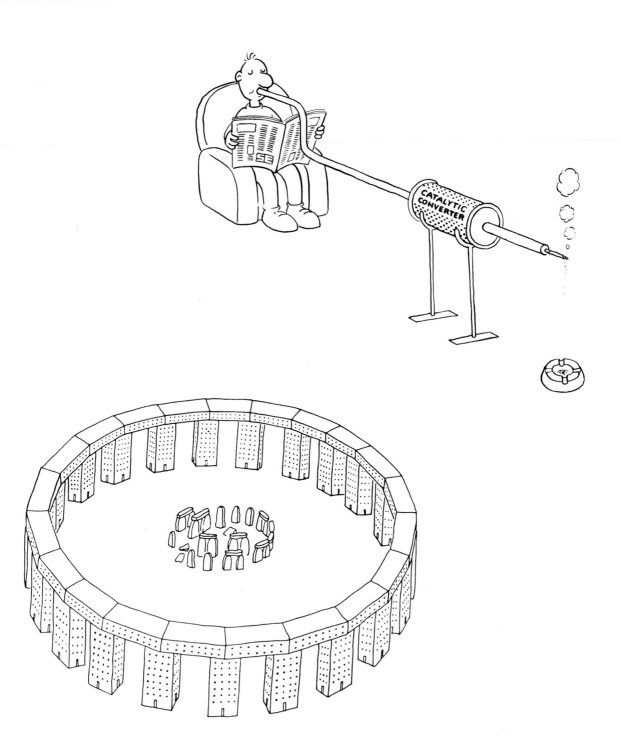

SELF DEFENSE CIRCA 1000 AD

SELF DEFENSE CIRCA 2000 AD

'He recycles everything'

'Looks like number 27's lifts are out of order again'

'I just love to hear an environmentalist talking dirty'

VIRGIN FOREST

'It must be around here somewhere'

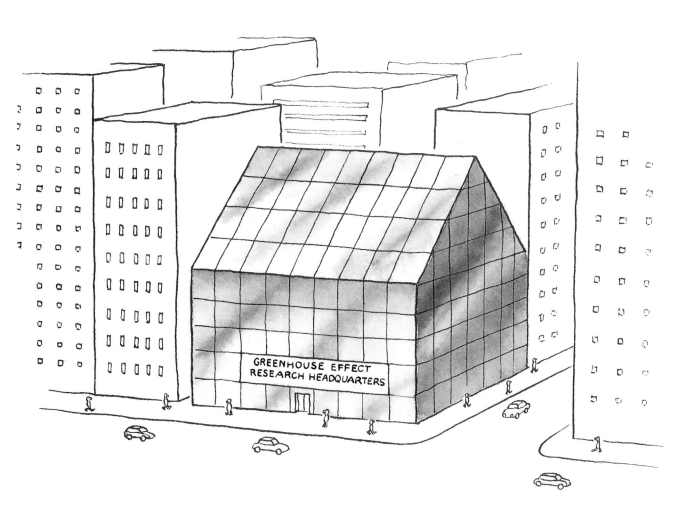

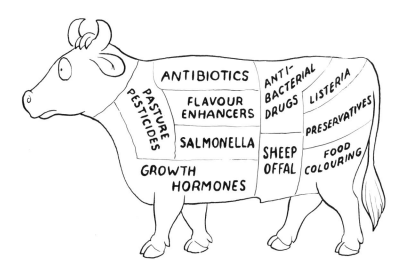

'The oil slick did wonders for
waterproofing the sand'

'If this food has no colourings, no flavourings,
no preservatives and no added sugar or salt, then
why does it cost more?'

'My girlfriend left me for some guy with
a catalytic converter'

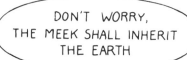

GOD SAVE US

from our own passivity

'One day son, all of this will be hamburgers'

'Trust you to go and stand in some growth hormone'

'Can't be too far from civilization now'

NATURE COULD SURVIVE WITHOUT ME
BUT I COULDN'T SURVIVE WITHOUT NATURE

'If you think they put too much junk in <u>our</u> food,
you should see what they put in their <u>own</u>'

RULE OF THUMB FOR FOOD ADDITIVES:

IF YOU CAN'T PRONOUNCE IT,
IT'S <u>BAD</u> FOR YOU

'Lovely sunset this evening'

'My god — I'm going green!'

'You're kidding — this is the stuff they wage wars over ?!'

'One day, with the money made by industry we'll be able to clean up the environment'

'He appears to have drastically reduced his carbon dioxide emissions'

'Mummy, where do hormones come from?'

'Bugger it — the acid rain has dissolved my biodegradable carrier bag'

'Hey, he's right — it is easy'

'Sylvia — how could you? You're using cruelty-free cosmetics!'

'Imagine the amount of advanced technological expertise
that went into producing this lot'

'We'll be extinct before you're finished!'

'I wouldn't if I were you'

'Hey, its not an oil slick after all
—its washed-off suntan lotion'

REBEL WITH TOO MANY CAUSES

SNIFF

'Mind if I smoke?'

'I wonder which is more environment friendly —
to buy a plastic Christmas tree
or to cut down a real one'

'Its acid snow'

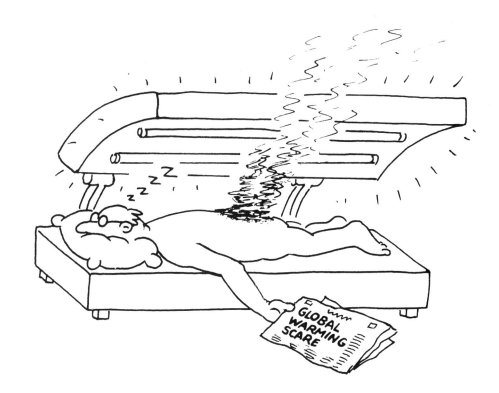